PLAY GUITAR WITH U2

(2000)

PLAY GUITAR WITH U2
(1992-2000)

Wise Publications
part of The Music Sales Group
London/New York/Paris/Sydney/Copenhagen/Berlin/Madrid/Tokyo

Published by
Wise Publications
8/9 Frith Street, London W1D 3JB, England

Exclusive Distributors:
Music Sales Limited
Distribution Centre, Newmarket Road, Bury St Edmunds, Suffolk IP33 3YB
Music Sales Pty Limited
120 Rothschild Avenue, Rosebery, NSW 2018, Australia

Order No. AM980826
ISBN 1-84449-664-3
This book © Copyright 2004 by Wise Publications

Compiled by Nick Crispin
Music arranged by Arthur Dick
Music processed by Paul Ewers Music Design
Project Editor: Tom Fleming
Printed in the United Kingdom

CD recorded, mixed and mastered by Jonas Persson
All guitars by Arthur Dick
Bass by Paul Townsend
Drums by Brett Morgan

Your Guarantee of Quality

*As publishers, we strive to produce
every book to the highest commercial standards.
The music has been freshly engraved and the book has
been carefully designed to minimise awkward page turns
and to make playing from it a real pleasure.
Particular care has been given to specifying acid-free,
neutral-sized paper made from pulps which have not been
elemental chlorine bleached. This pulp is from farmed
sustainable forests and was produced with
special regard for the environment.
Throughout, the printing and binding have been planned
to ensure a sturdy, attractive publication which
should give years of enjoyment.
If your copy fails to meet our high standards,
please inform us and we will gladly replace it.*

www.musicsales.com

Hold Me, Thrill Me, Kiss Me, Kill Me

Words & Music by U2

Tune guitars down a semitone

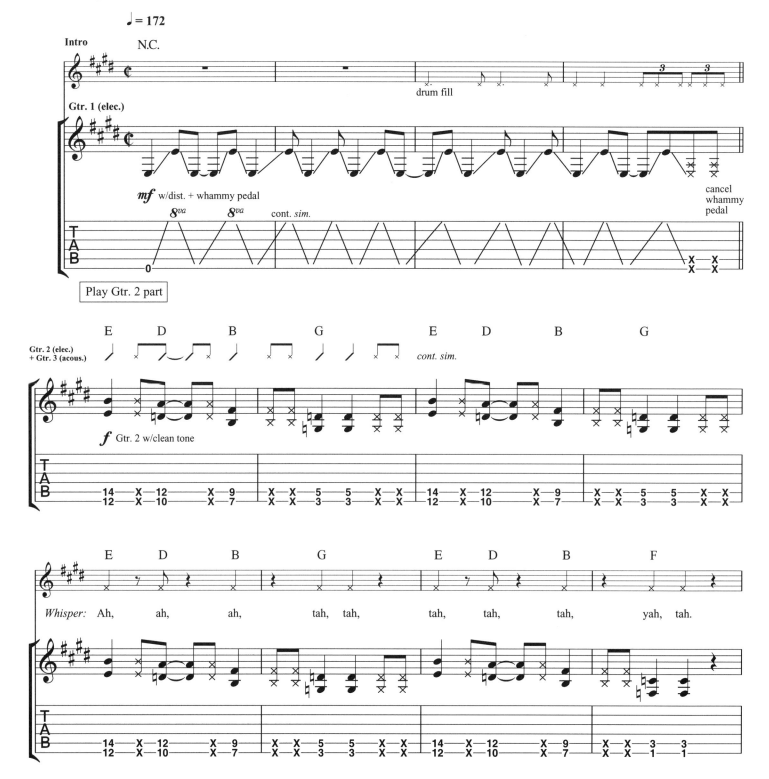

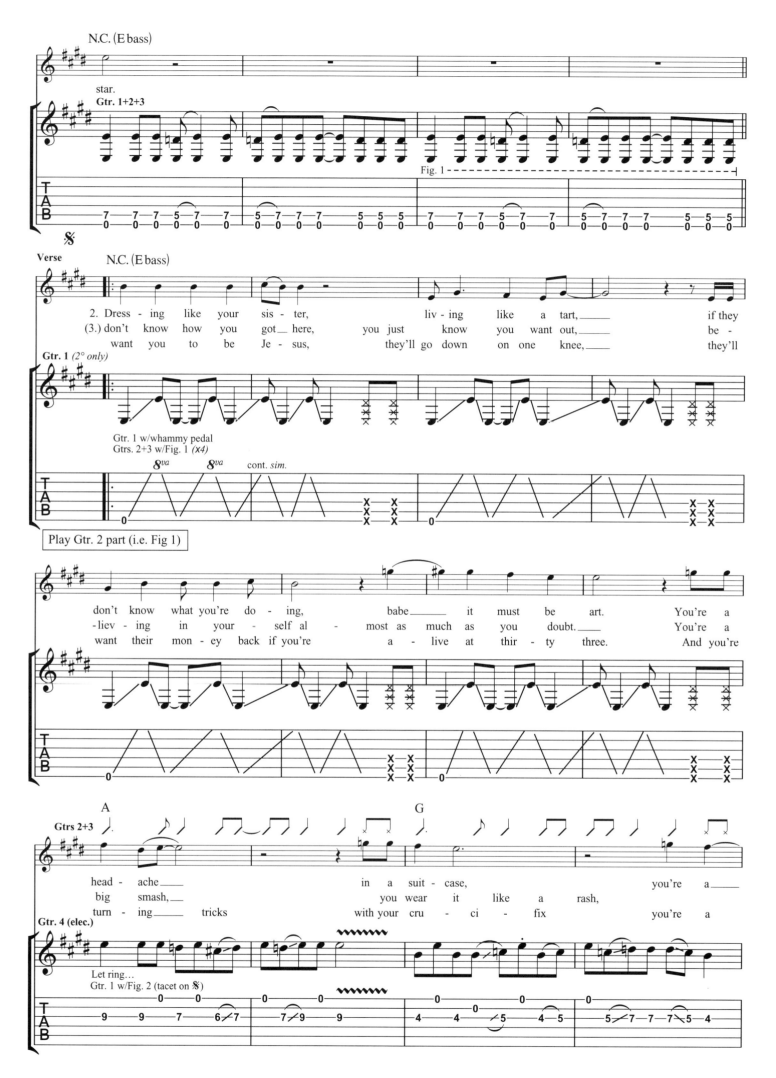

N.C. (E bass)

star.
Gtr. 1+2+3

Fig. 1

Verse   N.C. (E bass)

2. Dress - ing like your sis - ter, liv - ing like a tart,____ if they
(3.) don't know how you got__ here, you just know you want out,____ be -
want you to be Je - sus, they'll go down on one knee,____ they'll

Gtr. 1 (2° only)

Gtr. 1 w/whammy pedal
Gtrs. 2+3 w/Fig. 1 (x4)

8va   8va   cont. sim.

Play Gtr. 2 part (i.e. Fig 1)

don't know what you're do - ing, babe____ it must be art. You're a
-liev - ing in your - self al - most as much as you doubt.____ You're a
want their mon - ey back if you're a - live at thir - ty three. And you're

A   G

Gtrs 2+3

head - ache____ in a suit - case, you're a____
big smash,__ you wear it like a rash, you're a
turn - ing__ tricks with your cru - ci - fix you're a

Gtr. 4 (elec.)

Let ring...
Gtr. 1 w/Fig. 2 (tacet on 𝄋)

8

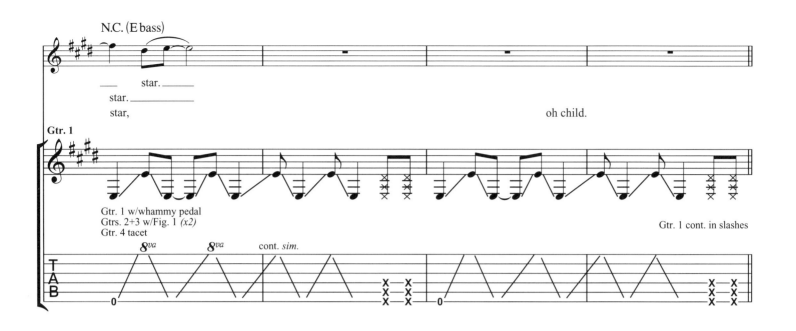

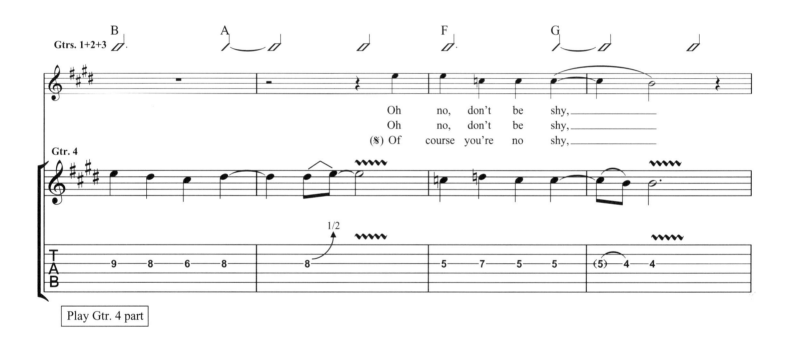

Play Gtr. 4 part

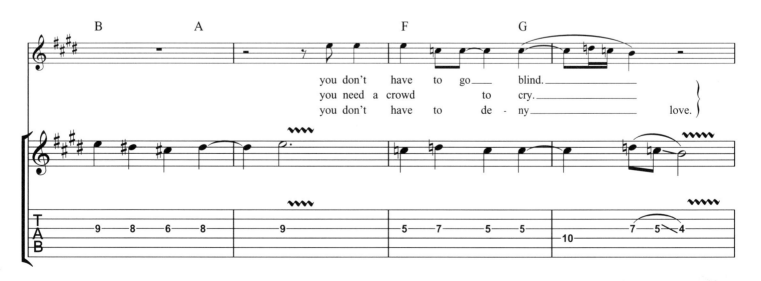

Discothèque

Words & Music by U2

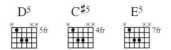

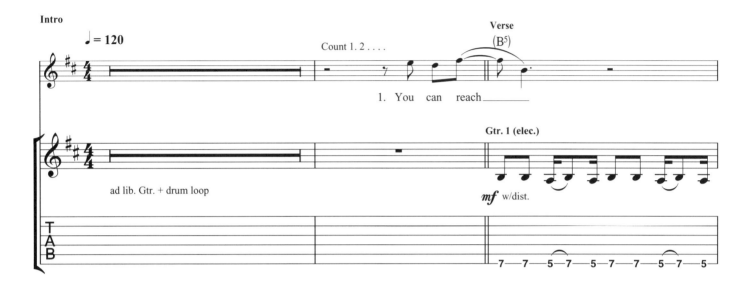

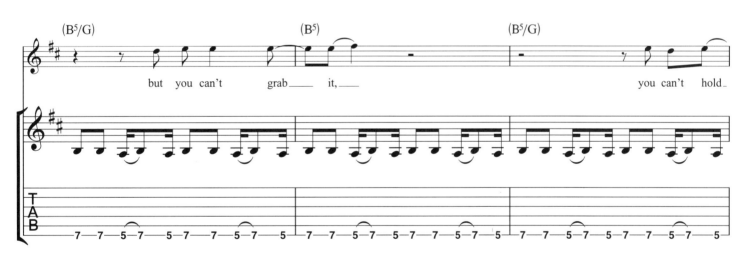

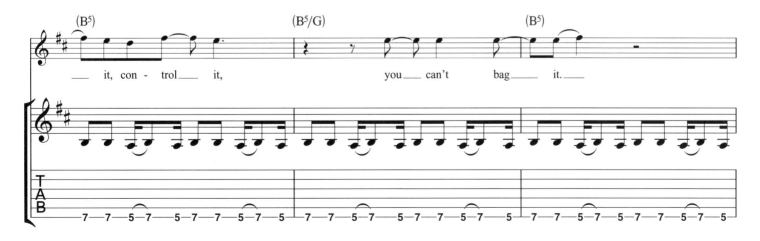

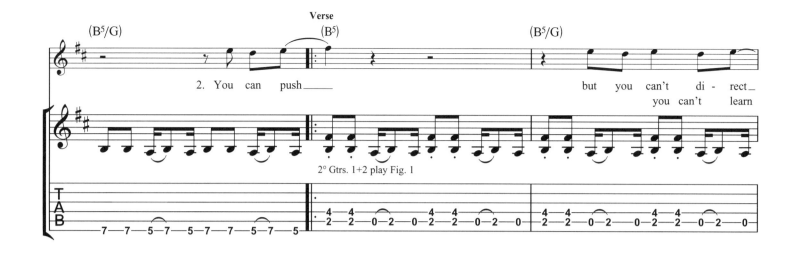

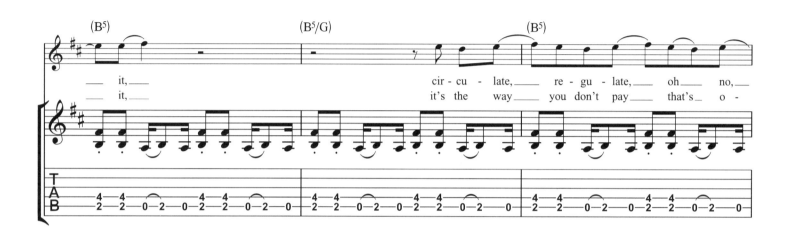

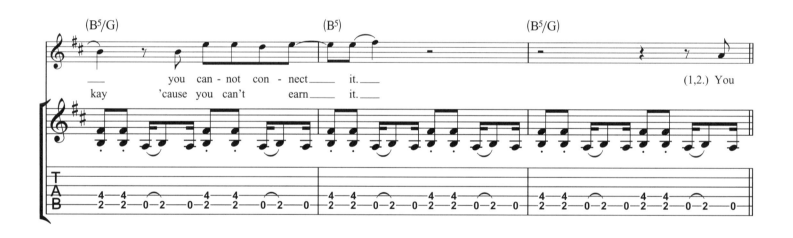

want some, you just can't get e - nough of that lov - ie dov - ie stuff.

1.

w/slight dist + delay
Fig. 1

You get con - fused

but you know it, yeah, you hurt

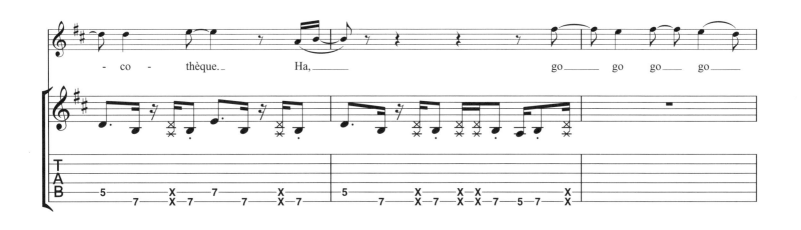

-co - thèque. Ha,_____ go_ go go_ go_

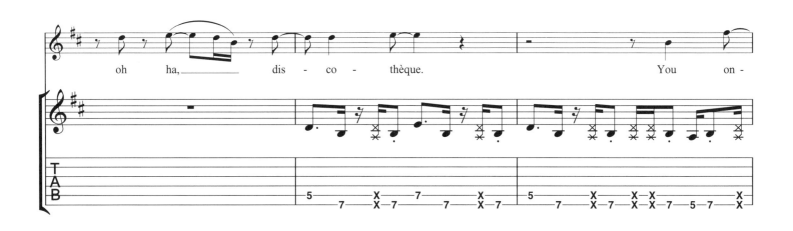

oh ha,_____ dis - co - thèque. You on -

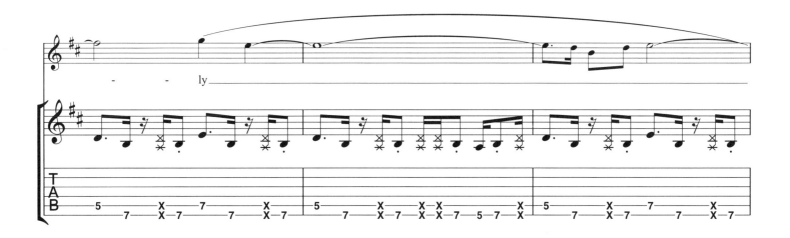

- ly_____

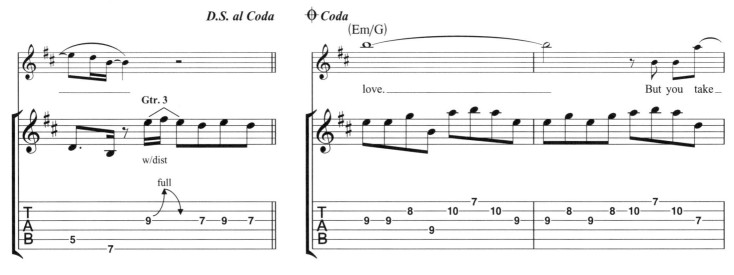

D.S. al Coda Coda

(Em/G)

love._____ But you take_

Gtr. 3

w/dist

full

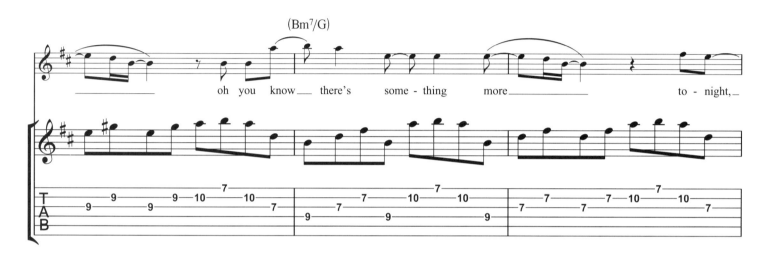

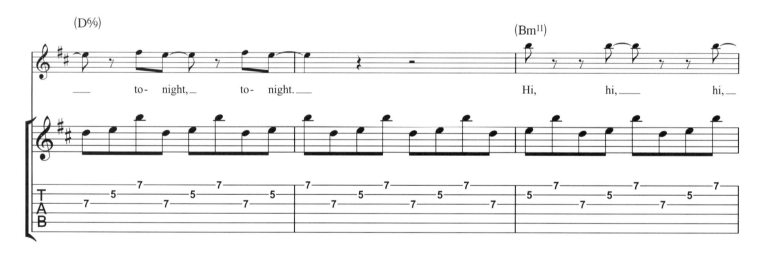

boom__ cha, boom__ cha, dis - co- tèque. boom__ cha, boom__

Outro

N.C.

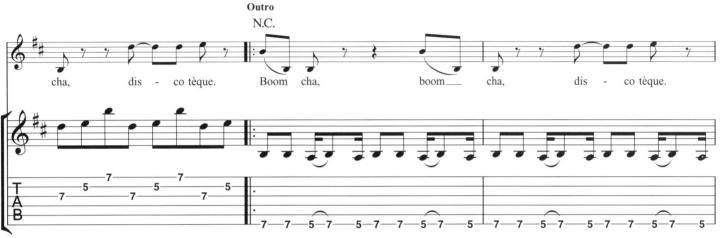

cha, dis - co tèque. Boom cha, boom__ cha, dis - co tèque.

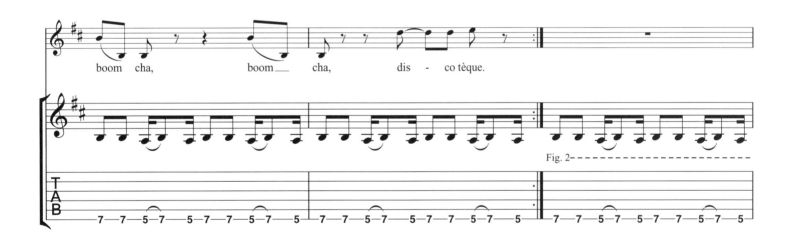

boom cha, boom__ cha, dis - co tèque.

Fig. 2- -

Repeat ad lib. to fade

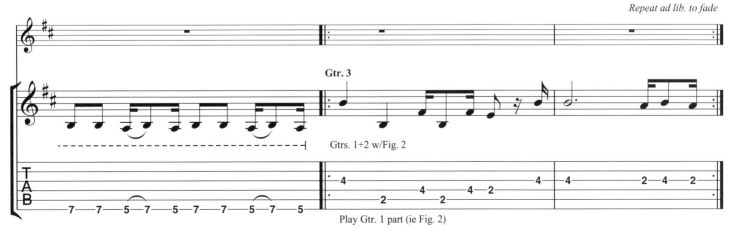

Gtrs. 1+2 w/Fig. 2

Gtr. 3

Play Gtr. 1 part (ie Fig. 2)

Beautiful Day

Words by Bono

Music by U2

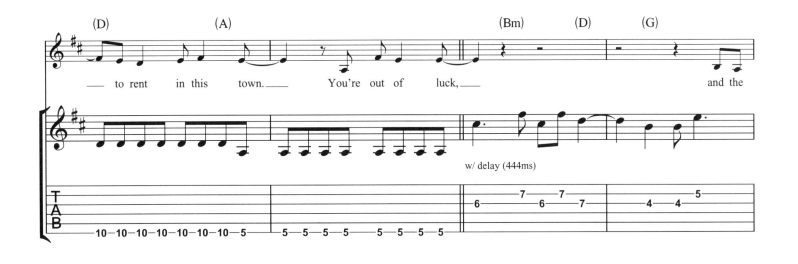

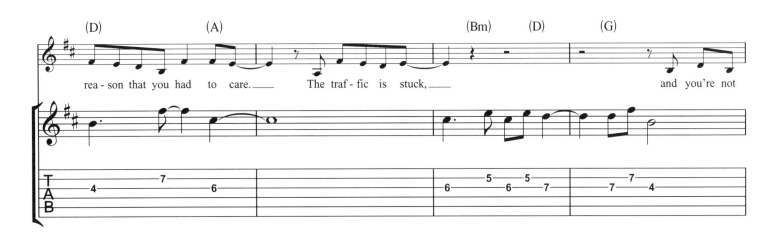

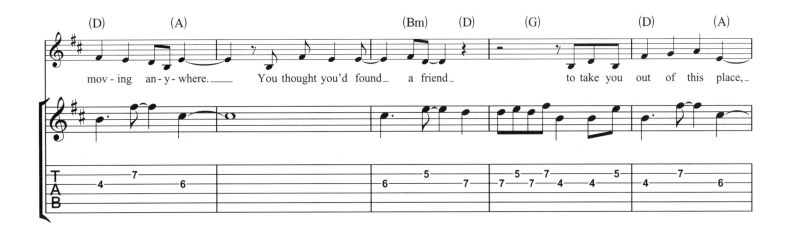

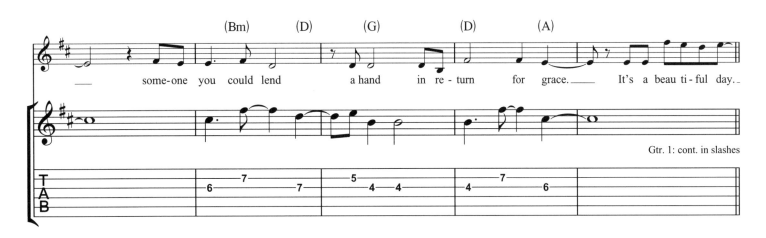

Stuck In A Moment
You Can't Get Out Of

Words by Bono & The Edge
Music by U2

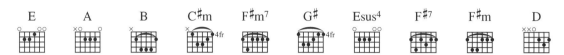

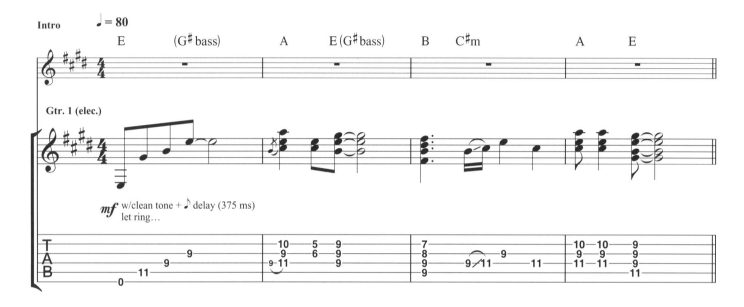

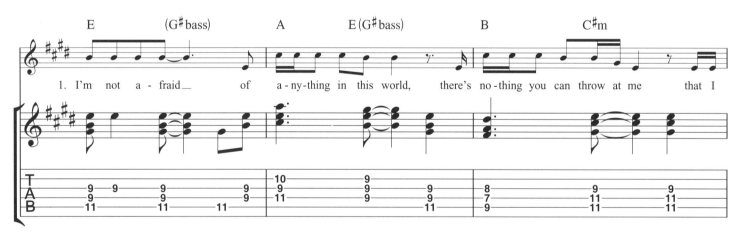

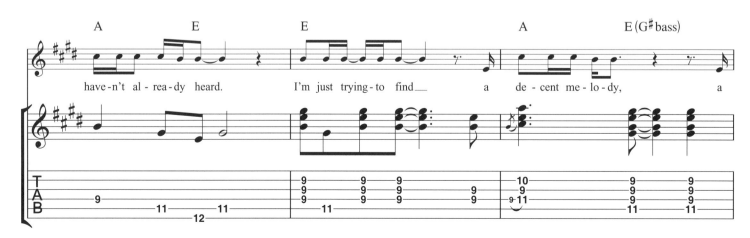

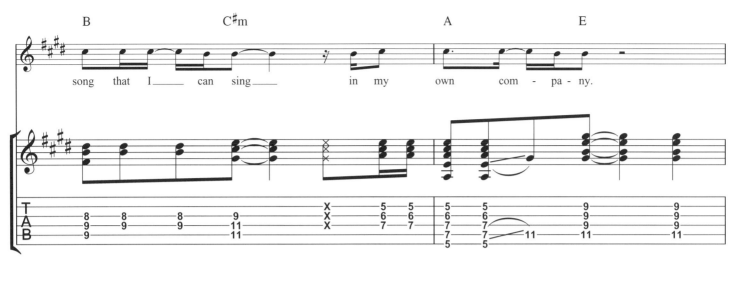

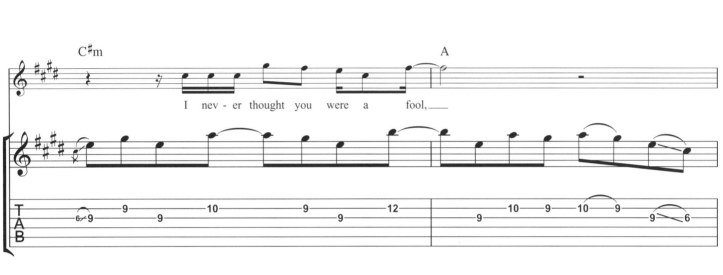

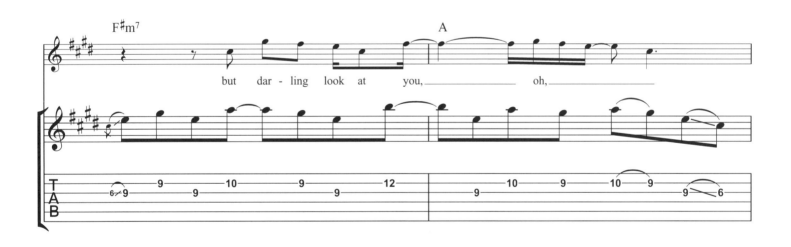

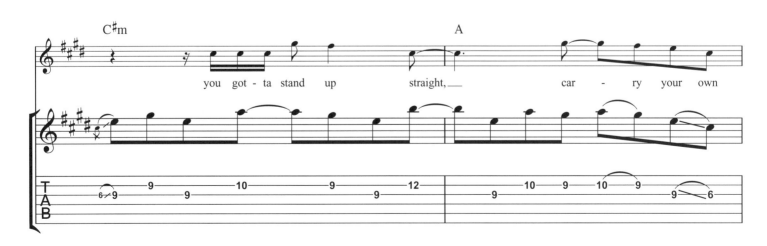

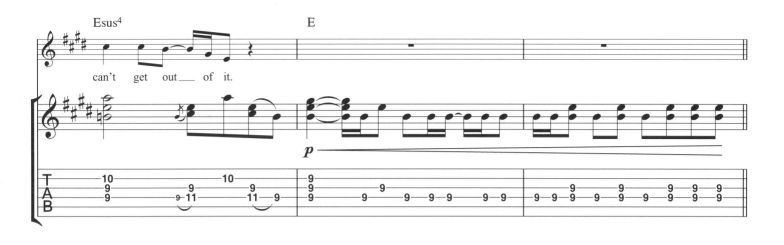

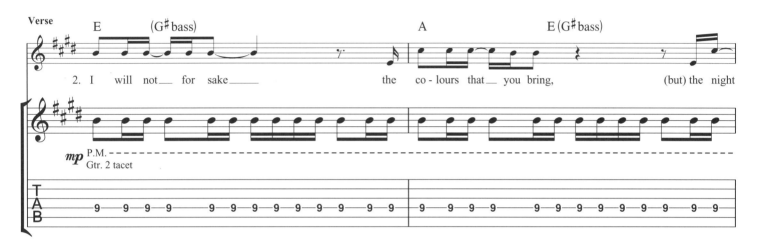

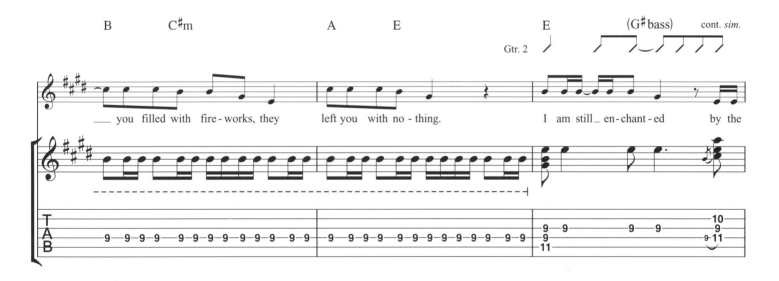

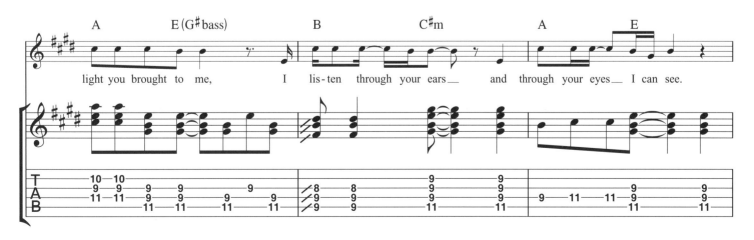

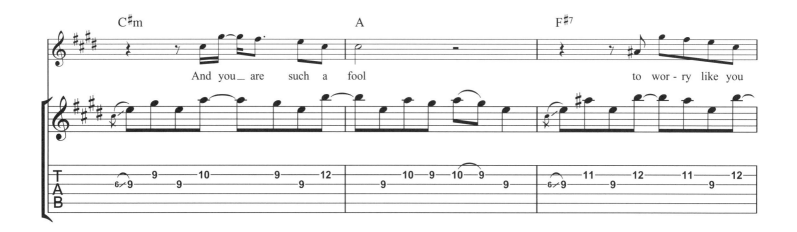

And you_ are such a fool to wor - ry like you

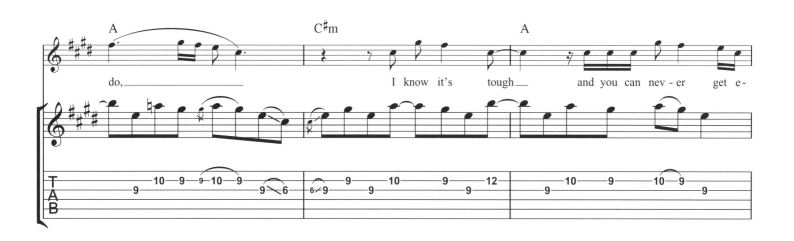

do,_____ I know it's tough__ and you can nev - er get e-

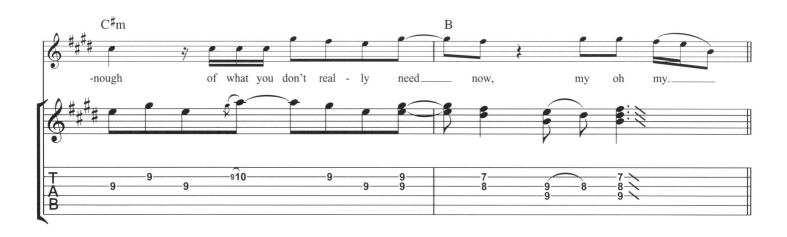

-nough of what you don't real - ly need___ now, my oh my.___

Chorus

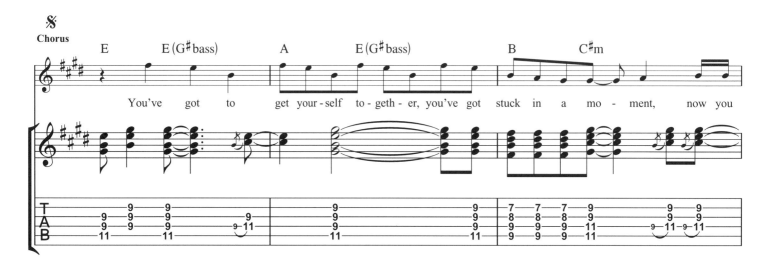

You've got to get your-self to - geth- er, you've got stuck in a mo-ment, now you

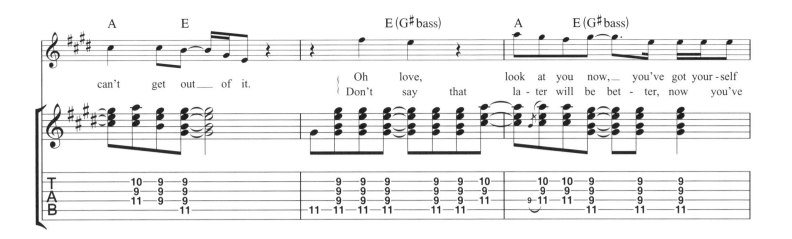

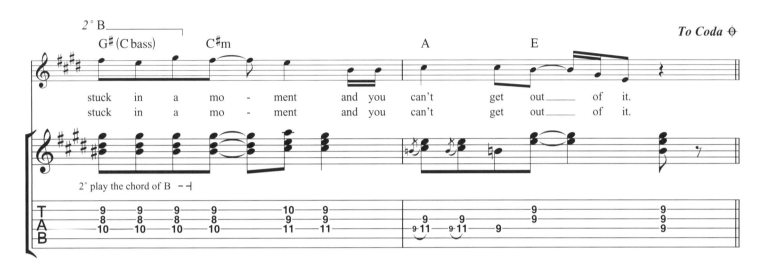

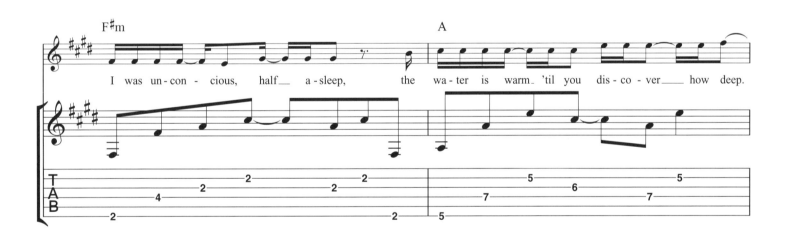

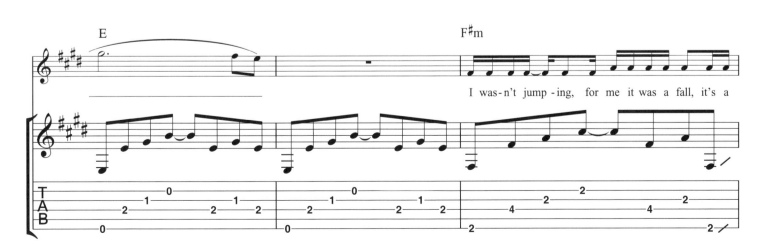

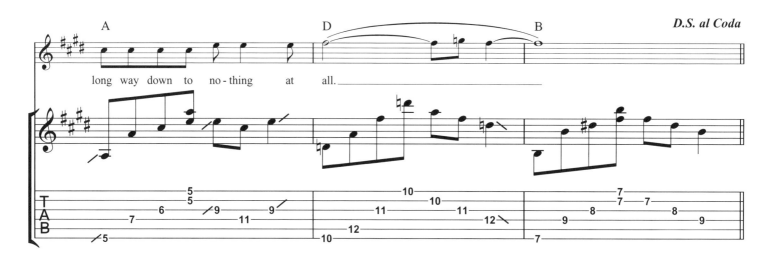

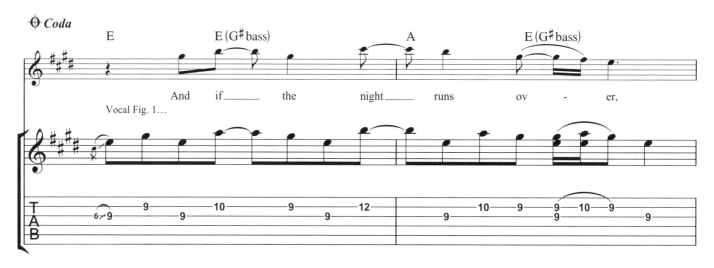

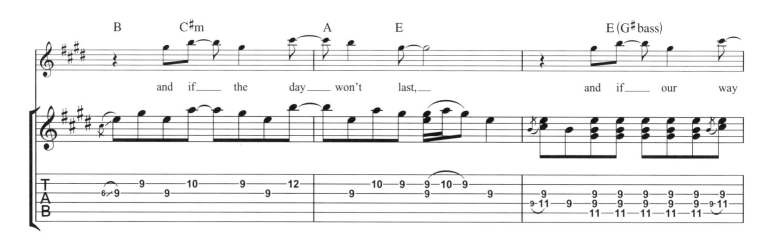

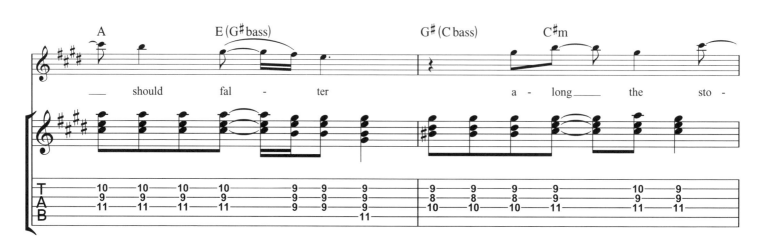

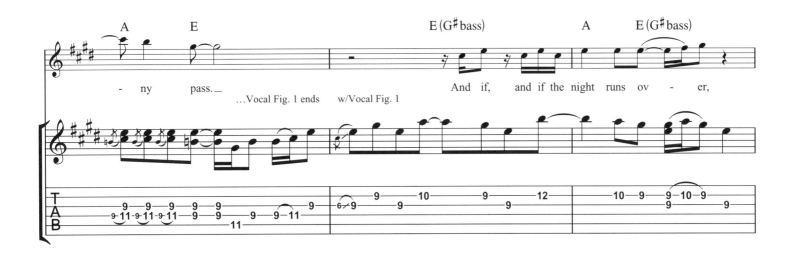

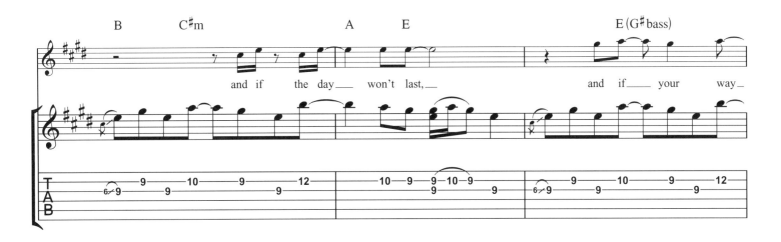

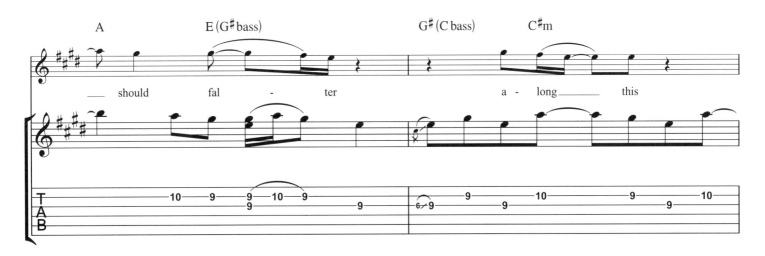

Elevation

Words by Bono
Music by U2

Verse

1. High, high-er than the sun, you shoot me from a gun, I need you to
(2.) star, lit up like a ci - gar, strung out like a gui - tar, may - be you could

Gtr. 1

mf w/octaver
*Gtrs. 2+3 tacet

* Play w/Gtr.1 - optional

e - le - vate me, here. At the cor - ner of your lips, as the or - bit of your
e - du - cate my mind. Ex - plain all these con - trols, (I) can't sing but I've got

hips, e - clipse, you e - le - vate my
soul, the goal is e - le - va - tion. A

Pre-chorus

soul. I've lost all self - con - trol, been liv - ing like a mole. Now, go - ing down,
2.(%) mole liv - ing in a hole, dig - ging up my soul go - ing down,

Gtrs. 1+2

sim.

ex - ca - va - tion. I and I in the sky,___ you make me feel like I can
ex - ca - va - tion. I and I in the sky,___ you make me feel like I can

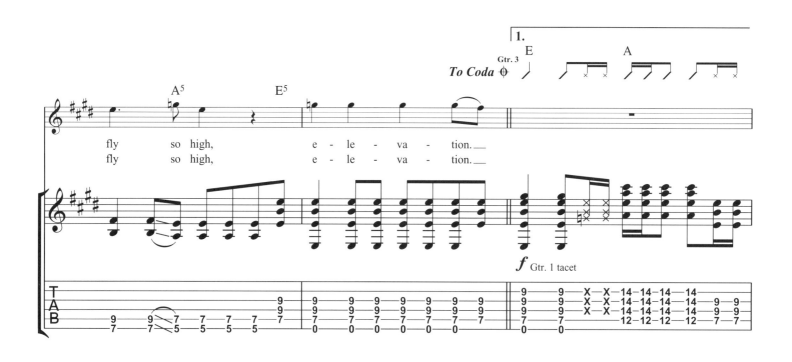

fly so high, e - le - va - tion.___
fly so high, e - le - va - tion.___

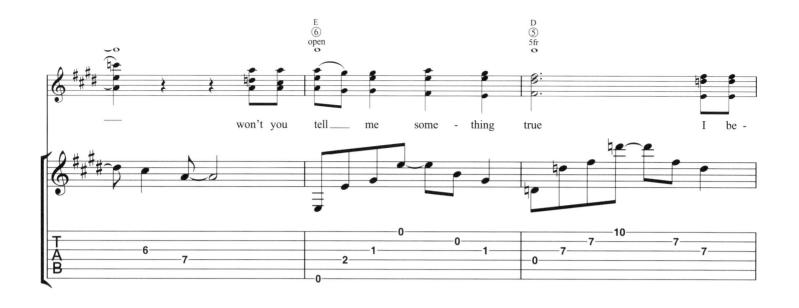

won't you tell___ me some - thing true   I be -

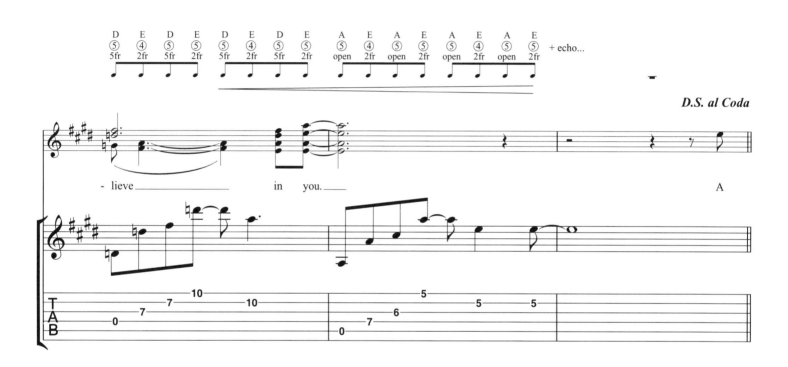

D.S. al Coda

- lieve_____ in you.___   A

E - le -va -tion.   E - le -va -tion.

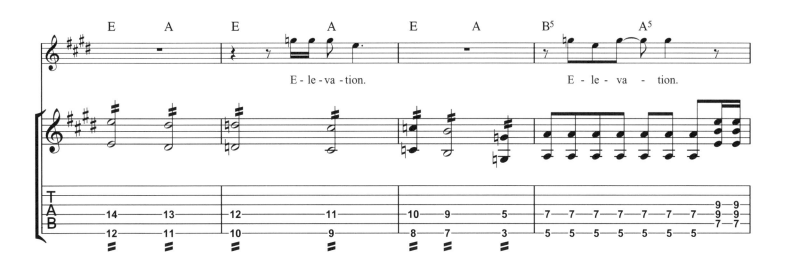

E - le - va - tion.

E - le - va - tion.

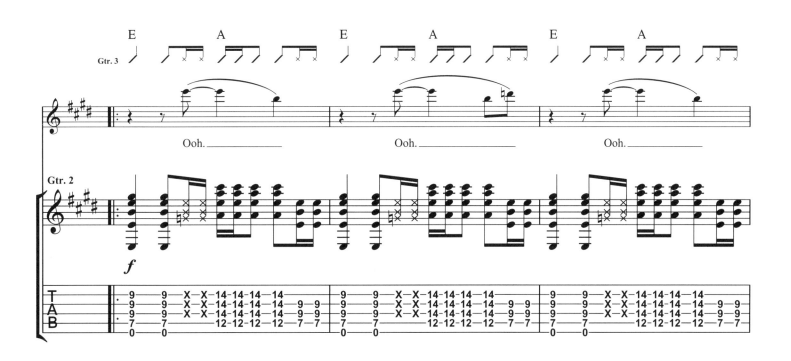

Ooh.

Ooh.

Ooh.

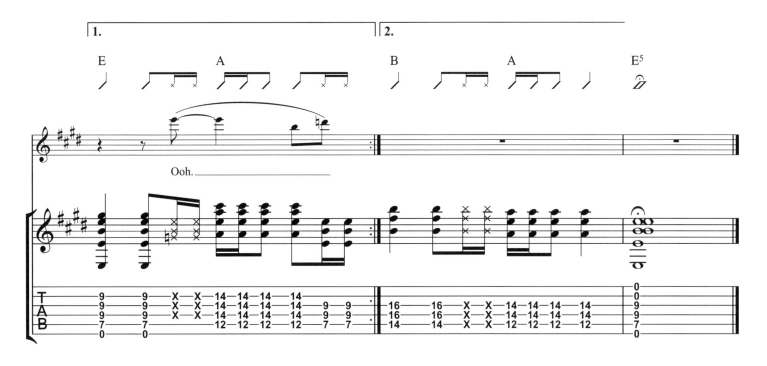

Ooh.

Last Night On Earth

Words & Music by U2

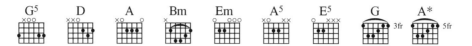

G⁵   D   A   Bm   Em   A⁵   E⁵   G   A*

Tune all Gtrs. down a semitone

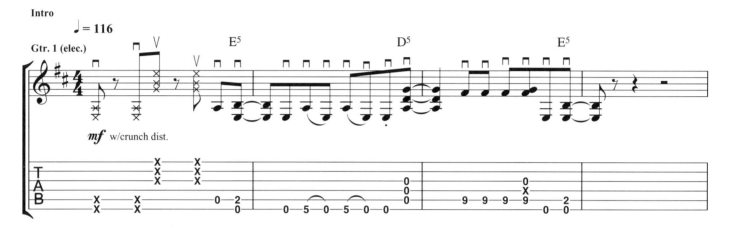

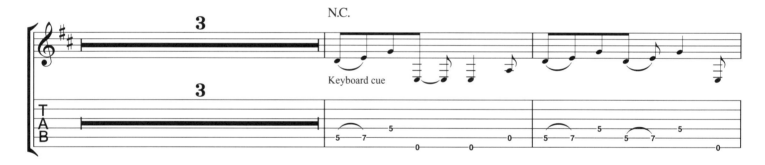

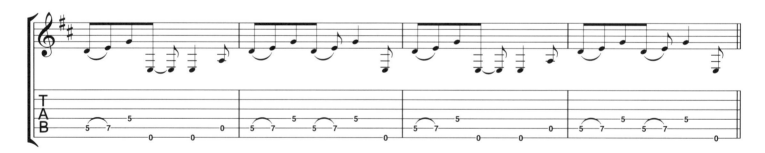

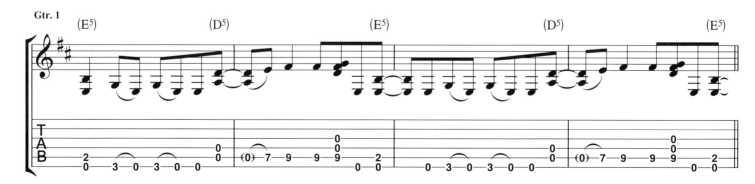

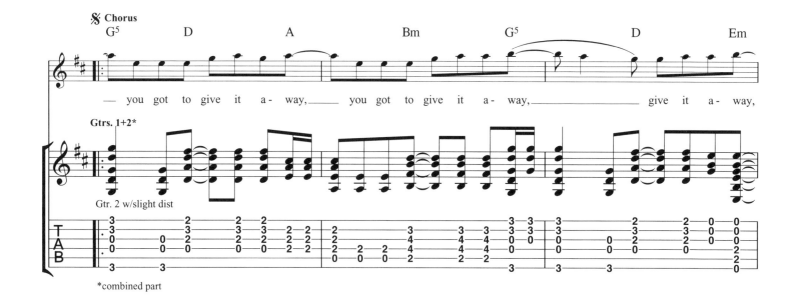

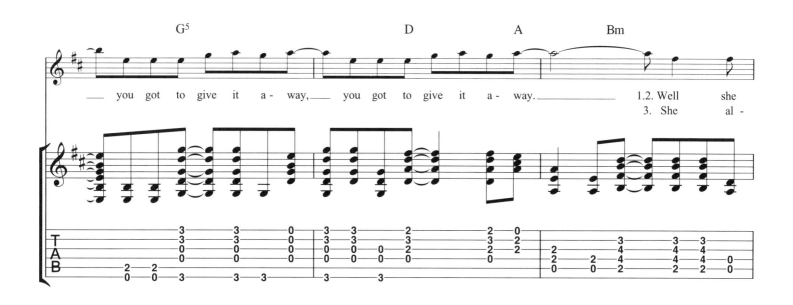

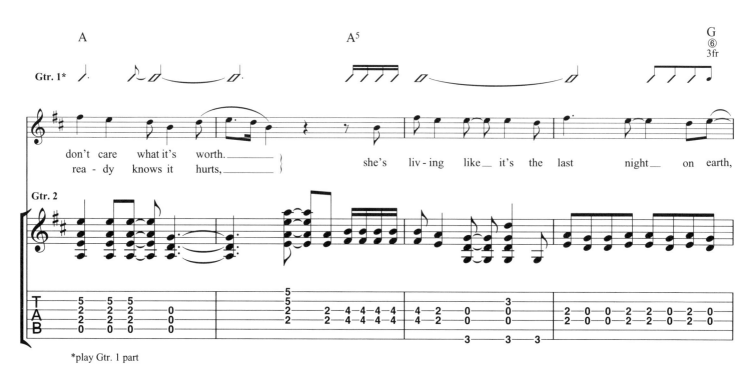

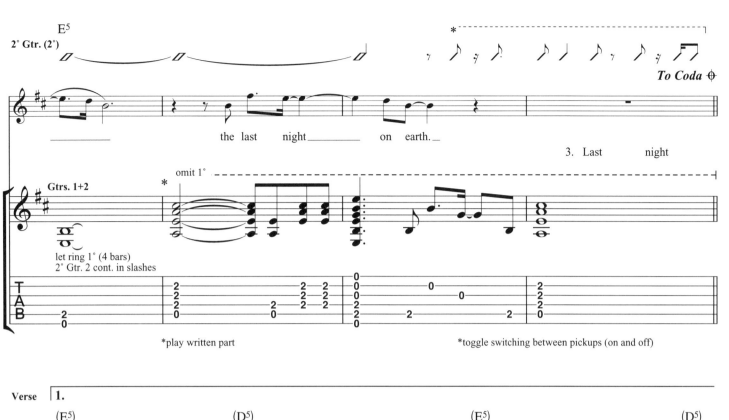

*play written part

*toggle switching between pickups (on and off)

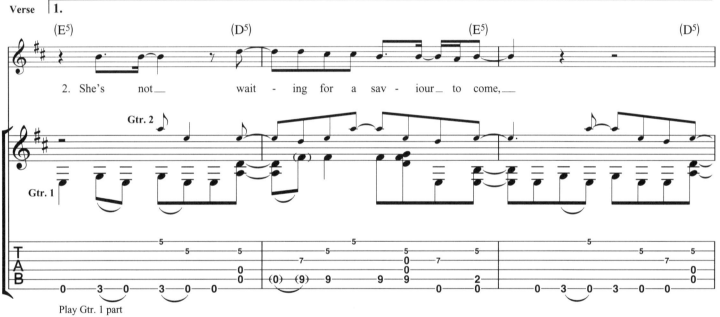

Play Gtr. 1 part

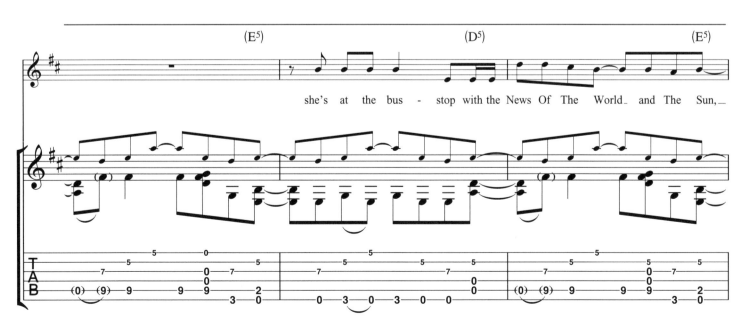

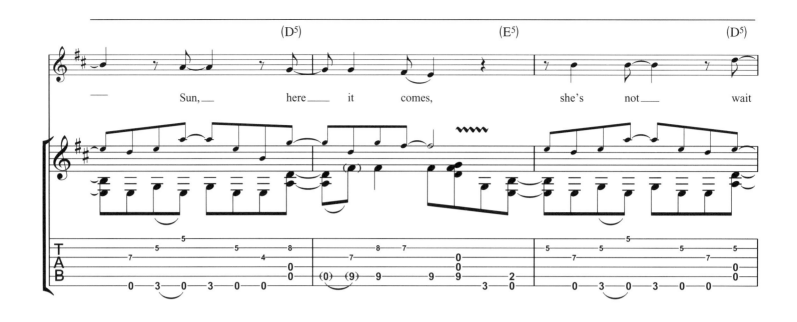

Sun,— here— it comes, she's not— wait

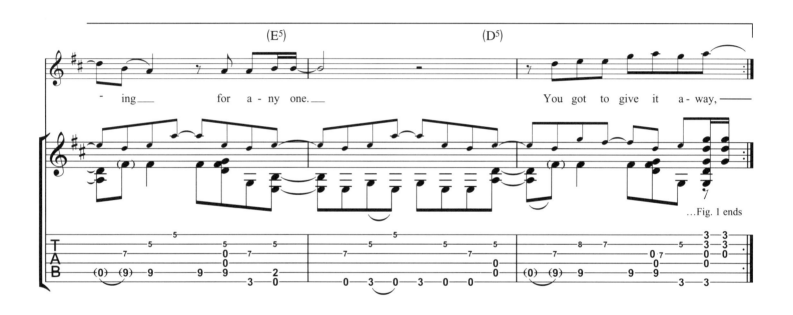

-ing— for a-ny one.— You got to give it a-way,—

...Fig. 1 ends

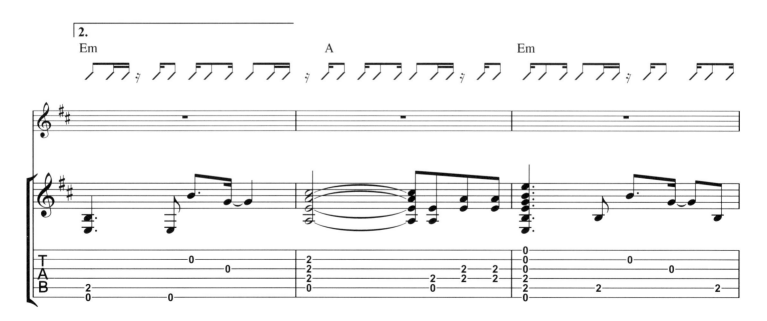

2.

Em   A   Em

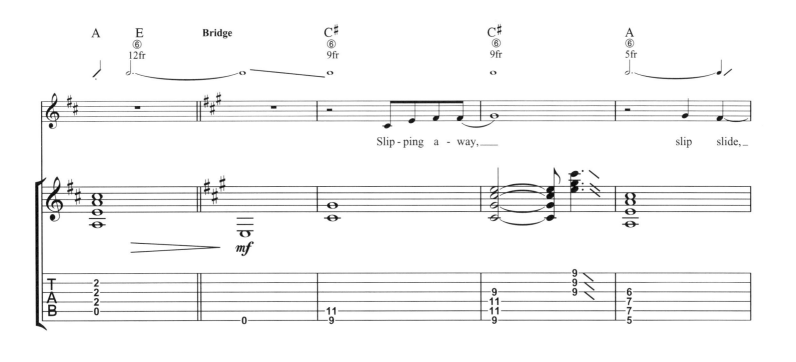

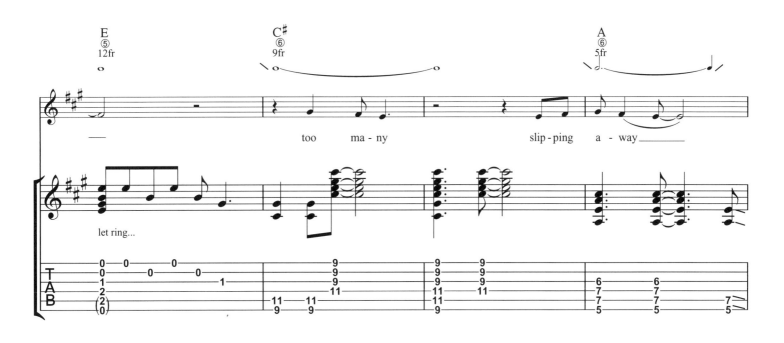

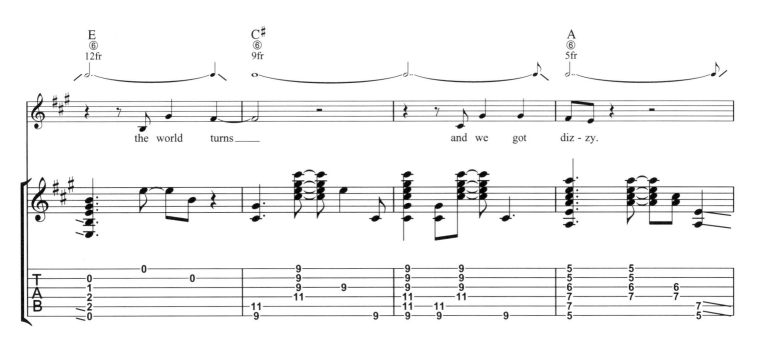

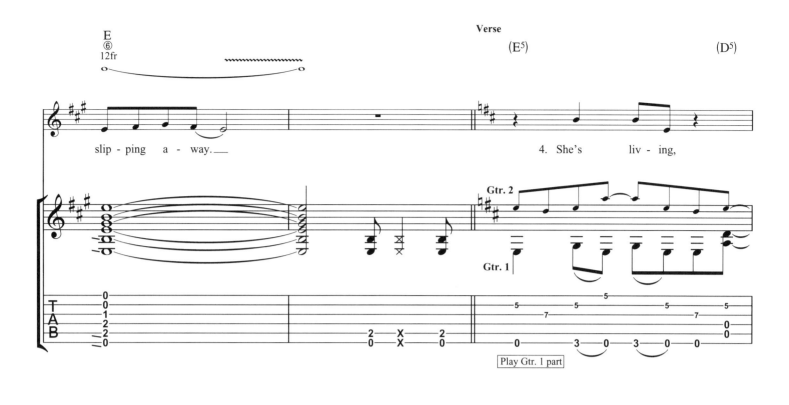

slip - ping a - way.___

4. She's liv - ing,

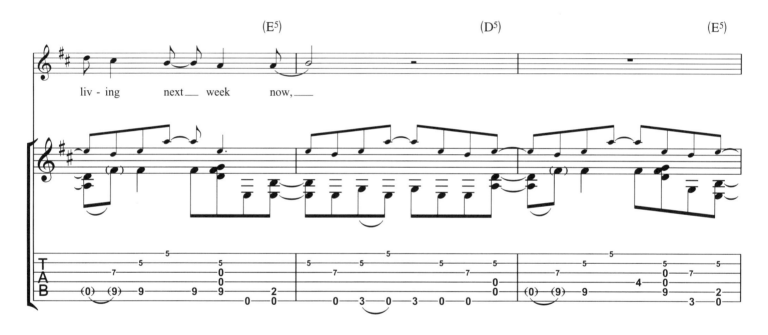

liv - ing next___ week now,___

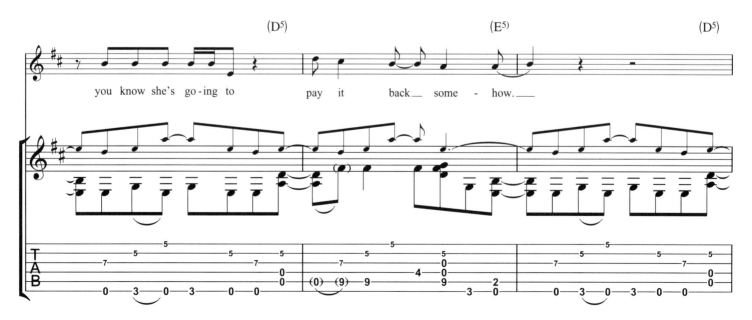

you know she's go - ing to pay it back___ some - how.___

50

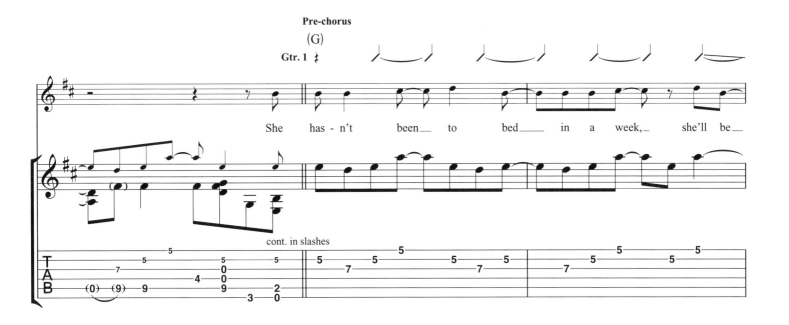

Pre-chorus

(G)

She has-n't been__ to bed__ in a week,__ she'll be__

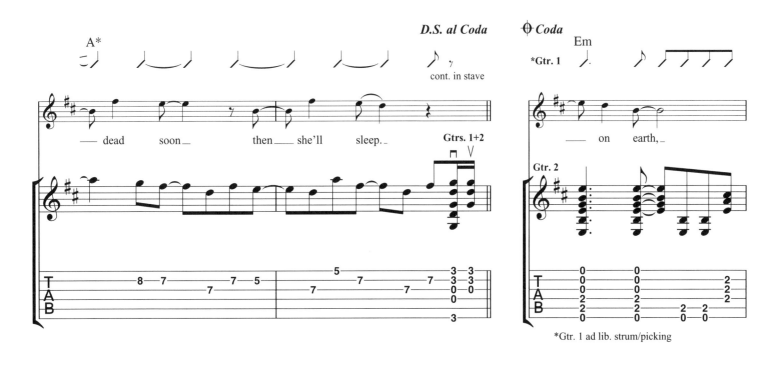

A*

D.S. al Coda   ⊕ Coda

— dead soon__ then__ she'll sleep.__

on earth,__

*Gtr. 1 ad lib. strum/picking

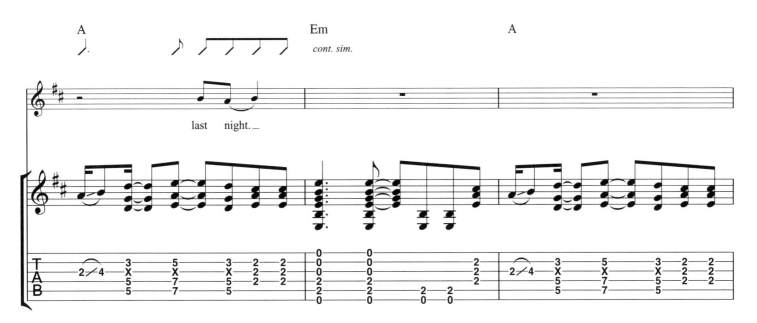

A   Em   A

last night.__

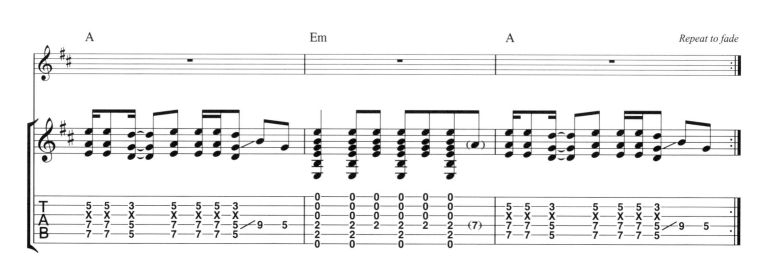

Walk On

Words by Bono
Music by U2

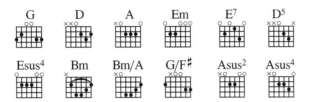

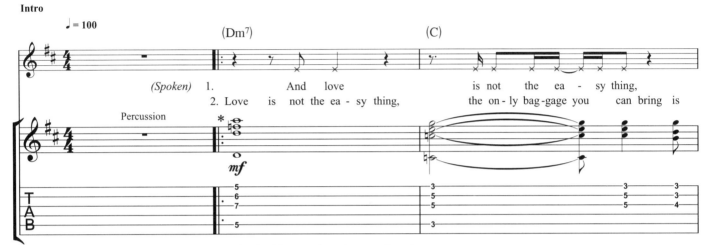

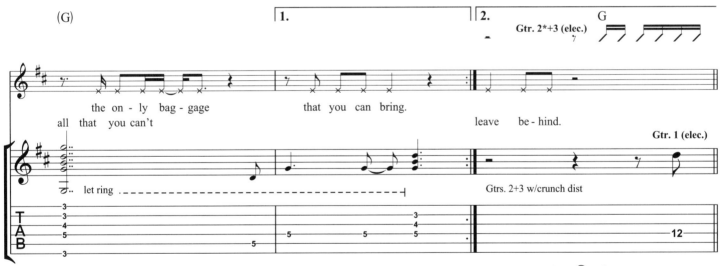

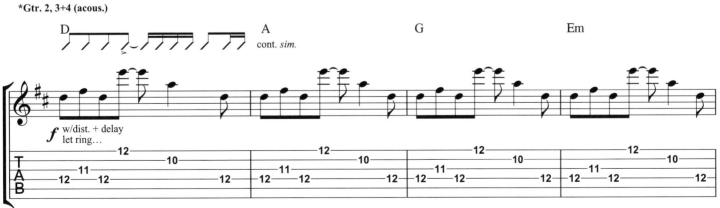

Chorus

where it is, ___ but I know ___ I'm go - ing home, ___

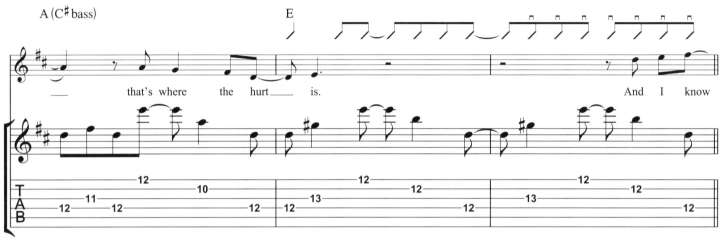

___ that's where the hurt ___ is. And I know

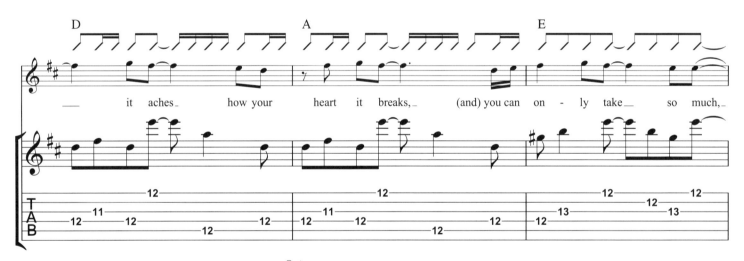

___ it aches ___ how your heart it breaks, ___ (and) you can on - ly take ___ so much, ___

Outro
*Gtrs. 2+3+4

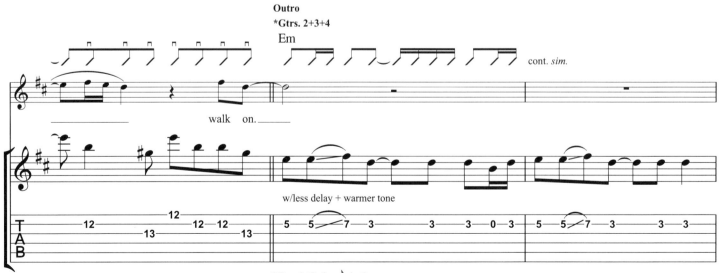

_____ walk on. ___

w/less delay + warmer tone

*Gtrs. 2+3 play ♪ rhythm

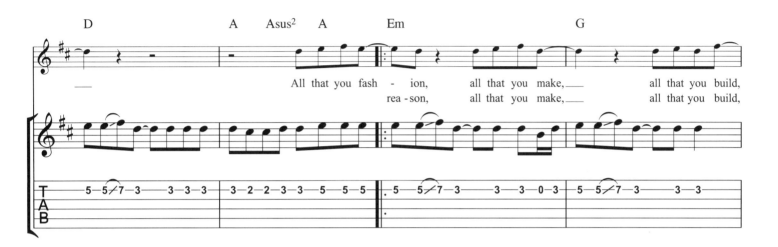

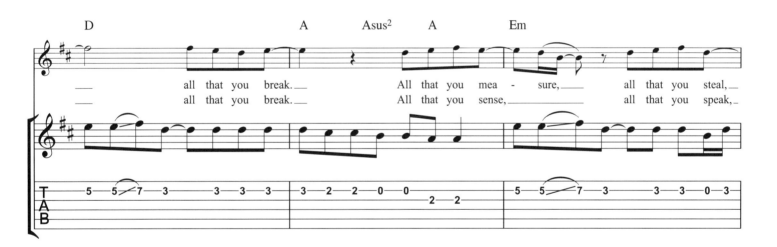

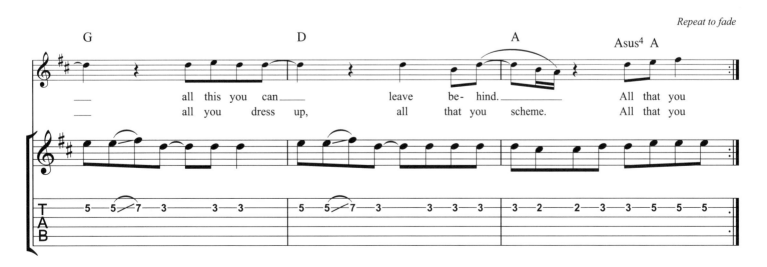

Guitar Tablature Explained

Guitar music can be notated in three different ways: on a musical stave, in tablature, and in rhythm slashes.

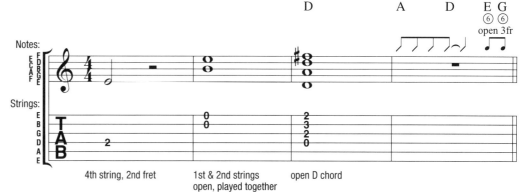

RHYTHM SLASHES are written above the stave. Strum chords in the rhythm indicated. Round noteheads indicate single notes.

THE MUSICAL STAVE shows pitches and rhythms and is divided by lines into bars. Pitches are named after the first seven letters of the alphabet.

TABLATURE graphically represents the guitar fingerboard. Each horizontal line represents a string, and each number represents a fret.

4th string, 2nd fret | 1st & 2nd strings open, played together | open D chord

Definitions For Special Guitar Notation

SEMI-TONE BEND: Strike the note and bend up a semi-tone (1/2 step).

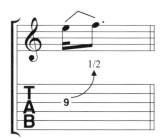

WHOLE-TONE BEND: Strike the note and bend up a whole-tone (whole step).

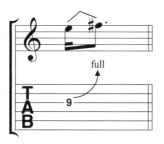

GRACE NOTE BEND: Strike the note and bend as indicated. Play the first note as quickly as possible.

QUARTER-TONE BEND: Strike the note and bend up a 1/4 step.

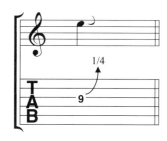

BEND & RELEASE: Strike the note and bend up as indicated, then release back to the original note.

COMPOUND BEND & RELEASE: Strike the note and bend up and down in the rhythm indicated.

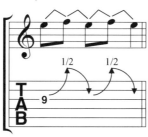

PRE-BEND: Bend the note as indicated, then strike it.

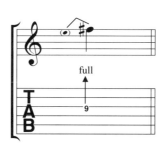

PRE-BEND & RELEASE: Bend the note as indicated. Strike it and release the note back to the original pitch.

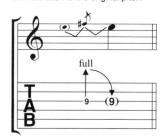

UNISON BEND: Strike the two notes simultaneously and bend the lower note up to the pitch of the higher.

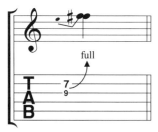

BEND & RESTRIKE: Strike the note and bend as indicated then restrike the string where the symbol occurs.

BEND, HOLD AND RELEASE: Same as bend and release but hold the bend for the duration of the tie.

BEND AND TAP: Bend the note as indicated and tap the higher fret while still holding the bend.

VIBRATO: The string is vibrated by rapidly bending and releasing the note with the fretting hand.

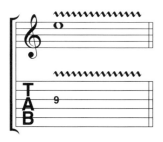

HAMMER-ON: Strike the first note with one finger, then sound the second note (on the same string) with another finger by fretting it without picking.

PULL-OFF: Place both fingers on the notes to be sounded, strike the first note and without picking, pull the finger off to sound the second note.

LEGATO SLIDE (GLISS): Strike the first note and then slide the same fret-hand finger up or down to the second note. The second note is not struck.

NOTE: The speed of any bend is indicated by the music notation and tempo.

SHIFT SLIDE (GLISS & RESTRIKE): Same as legato slide, except the second note is struck.

TRILL: Very rapidly alternate between the notes indicated by continuously hammering on and pulling off.

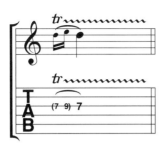

TAPPING: Hammer ("tap") the fret indicated with the pick-hand index or middle finger and pull off to the note fretted by the fret hand.

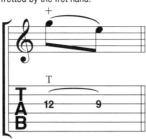

PICK SCRAPE: The edge of the pick is rubbed down (or up) the string, producing a scratchy sound.

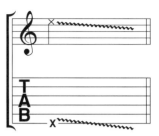

MUFFLED STRINGS: A percussive sound is produced by laying the fret hand across the string(s) without depressing, and striking them with the pick hand.

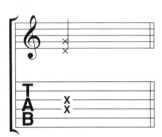

NATURAL HARMONIC: Strike the note while the fret-hand lightly touches the string directly over the fret indicated.

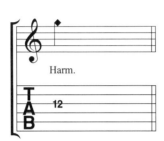

PINCH HARMONIC: The note is fretted normally and a harmonic is produced by adding the edge of the thumb or the tip of the index finger of the pick hand to the normal pick attack.

HARP HARMONIC: The note is fretted normally and a harmonic is produced by gently resting the pick hand's index finger directly above the indicated fret (in brackets) while plucking the appropriate string.

PALM MUTING: The note is partially muted by the pick hand lightly touching the string(s) just before the bridge.

RAKE: Drag the pick across the strings indicated with a single motion.

TREMOLO PICKING: The note is picked as rapidly and continuously as possible.

ARPEGGIATE: Play the notes of the chord indicated by quickly rolling them from bottom to top.

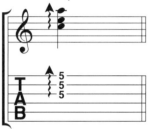

SWEEP PICKING: Rhythmic downstroke and/or upstroke motion across the strings.

VIBRATO DIVE BAR AND RETURN: The pitch of the note or chord is dropped a specific number of steps (in rhythm) then returned to the original pitch.

VIBRATO BAR SCOOP: Depress the bar just before striking the note, then quickly release the bar.

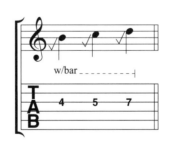

VIBRATO BAR DIP: Strike the note and then immediately drop a specific number of steps, then release back to the original pitch.

additional musical definitions

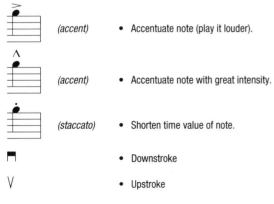

(accent)	•	Accentuate note (play it louder).
(accent)	•	Accentuate note with great intensity.
(staccato)	•	Shorten time value of note.
	•	Downstroke
	•	Upstroke

NOTE: Tablature numbers in brackets mean:
1. The note is sustained, but a new articulation (such as hammer on or slide) begins.
2. A note may be fretted but not necessarily played.

D.%. al Coda

D.C. al Fine

tacet

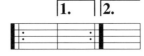

• Go back to the sign (%), then play until the bar marked *To Coda* ⊕ then skip to the section marked ⊕ *Coda*.

• Go back to the beginning of the song and play until the bar marked *Fine*.

• Instrument is silent (drops out).

• Repeat bars between signs.

• When a repeated section has different endings, play the first ending only the first time and the second ending only the second time.

Présentation De La Tablature De Guitare

Il existe trois façons différentes de noter la musique pour guitare : à l'aide d'une portée musicale, de tablatures ou de barres rythmiques.

Les **BARRES RYTHMIQUES** sont indiquées au-dessus de la portée. Jouez les accords dans le rythme indiqué. Les notes rondes indiquent des notes réciles.

La **PORTÉE MUSICALE** indique les notes et rythmes et est divisée en mesures. Cette division est représentée par des lignes. Les notes sont : do, ré, mi, fa, sol, la, si.

La **PORTÉE EN TABLATURE** est une représentation graphique des touches de guitare. Chaque ligne horizontale correspond à une corde et chaque chiffre correspond à une case.

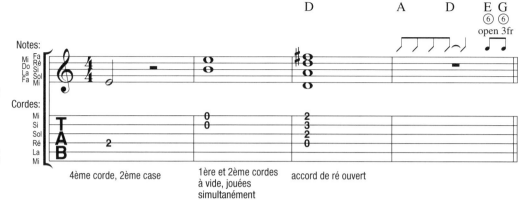

4ème corde, 2ème case

1ère et 2ème cordes à vide, jouées simultanément

accord de ré ouvert

Notation Spéciale De Guitare : Définitions

TIRÉ DEMI-TON : Jouez la note et tirez la corde afin d'élever la note d'un demi-ton (étape à moitié).

TIRÉ PLEIN : Jouez la note et tirez la corde afin d'élever la note d'un ton entier (étape entière).

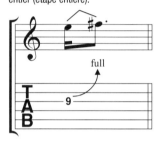

TIRÉ D'AGRÉMENT : Jouez la note et tirez la corde comme indiqué. Jouez la première note aussi vite que possible.

TIRÉ QUART DE TON : Jouez la note et tirez la corde afin d'élever la note d'un quart de ton.

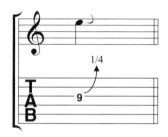

TIRÉ ET LÂCHÉ : Jouez la note et tirez la corde comme indiqué, puis relâchez, afin d'obtenir de nouveau la note de départ.

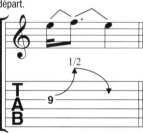

TIRÉ ET REJOUÉ : Jouez la note et tirez la corde comme indiqué puis rejouez la corde où le symbole apparaît.

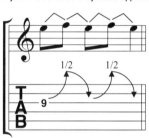

PRÉ-TIRÉ : Tirez la corde comme indiqué puis jouez cette note.

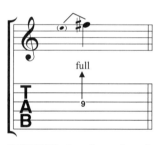

PRÉ-TIRÉ ET LÂCHÉ : Tirez la corde comme indiqué. Jouez la note puis relâchez la corde afin d'obtenir le ton de départ.

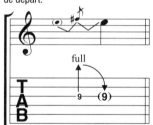

HAMMER-ON : Jouez la première note (plus basse) avec un doigt puis jouez la note plus haute sur la même corde avec un autre doigt, sur le manche mais sans vous servir du médiator.

h Positionnez deux doigts sur les notes à jouer. Jouez la première note et sans vous servir du médiator, dégagez un doigt pour obtenir la deuxième note, plus basse.

GLISSANDO : Jouez la première note puis faites glisser le doigt le long du manche pour obtenir la seconde note qui, elle, n'est pas jouée.

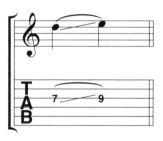

GLISSANDO ET REJOUÉ : Identique au glissando à ceci près que la seconde note est jouée.

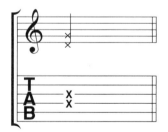

HARMONIQUES NATURELLES : Jouez la note tandis qu'un doigt effleure la corde sur le manche correspondant à la case indiquée.

PICK SCRAPE (SCRATCH) : On fait glisser le médiator le long de la corde, ce qui produit un son éraillé.

ÉTOUFFÉ DE LA PAUME : La note est partiellement étouffée par la main (celle qui se sert du médiator). Elle effleure la (les) corde(s) juste au-dessus du chevalet.

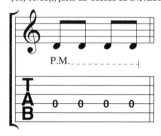

CORDES ÉTOUFFÉES : Un effet de percussion produit en posant à plat la main sur le manche sans relâcher, puis en jouant les cordes avec le médiator.

NOTE : La vitesse des tirés est indiquée par la notation musicale et le tempo.

Erläuterung zur Tabulaturschreibweise

Es gibt drei Möglichkeiten, Gitarrenmusik zu notieren: im klassichen Notensystem, in Tabulaturform oder als rhythmische Akzente.

RHYTHMISCHE AKZENTE werden über dem Notensystem notiert. Geschlagene Akkorde werden rhythmisch dargestellt. Ausgeschriebene Noten stellen Einzeltöne dar.

Im NOTENSYSTEM werden Tonhöhe und rhythmischer Verlauf festgelegt; es ist durch Taktstriche in Takte unterteilt. Die Töne werden nach den ersten acht Buchstaben des Alphabets benannt.
Beachte: "B" in der anglo-amerkanischen Schreibweise entspricht dem deutschen "H"!

DIE TABULATUR ist die optische Darstellung des Gitarrengriffbrettes. Jeder horizontalen Linie ist eine bestimmte Saite zugeordnet, jede Zahl bezeichnet einen Bund.

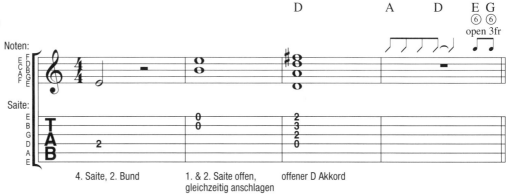

4. Saite, 2. Bund | 1. & 2. Saite offen, gleichzeitig anschlagen | offener D Akkord

Erklärungen zur speziellen Gitarennotation

HALBTON-ZIEHER: Spiele die Note und ziehe dann um einen Halbton höher (Halbtonschritt).

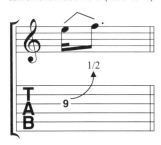

ZIEHEN UND ZURÜCKGLEITEN: Spiele die Note und ziehe wie notiert; lasse den Finger dann in die Ausgangposition zurückgleiten. Dabei wird nur die erste Note angeschlagen.

AUFSCHLAGTECHNIK: Schlage die erste (tiefere) Note an; die höhere Note (auf der selben Saite) erklingt durch kräftiges Aufschlagen mit einem anderen Finger der Griffhand.

NATÜRLICHES FLAGEOLETT: Berühre die Saite über dem angegebenen Bund leicht mit einem Finger der Griffhand. Schlage die Saite an und lasse sie frei schwingen.

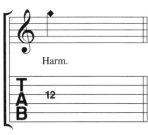

GANZTON-ZIEHER: Spiele die Note und ziehe dann einen Ganzton höher (Ganztonschritt).

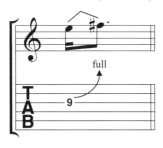

ZIEHEN UND NOCHMALIGES ANSCHLAGEN: Spiele die Note und ziehe die Siete wie notiert.

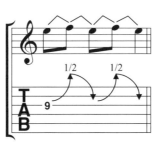

ABZIEHTECHNIK: Setze beide Finger auf die zu spielenden Noten und schlage die erste Note an. Ziehe dann (ohne nochmals anzuschlagen) den oberen Finger der Griffhand seitlich - abwärts ab, um die zweite (tiefere) Note zum klingen zu bringen.

PICK SCRAPE: Fahre mit dem Plektrum nach unten über die Saiten - klappt am besten bei umsponnenen Saiten.

ZIEHER MIT VORSCHLAG: Spiele die Note und ziehe wie notiert. Spiele die erste Note so schnell wie möglich.

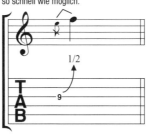

ZIEHER VOR DEM ANSCHLAGEN: Ziehe zuerst die Note wie notiert; schlage die Note dann an.

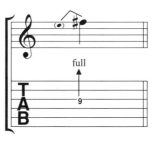

GLISSANDOTECHNIK: Schlage die erste Note an und rutsche dann mit dem selben Finger der Griffhand aufwärts oder abwärts zur zweiten Note. Die zweite Note wird nicht angeschlagen.

DÄMPFEN MIT DER SCHLAGHAND: Lege die Schlaghand oberhalb der Brücke leicht auf die Saite(n).

VIERTELTON-ZIEHER: Spiele die Note und ziehe dann einen Viertelton höher (Vierteltonschritt).

ZIEHER VOR DEM ANSCHLAGEN MIT ZURÜCKGLEITEN: Ziehe die Note wie notiert; schlage die Note dann an und lasse den Finger auf die Ausgangslage zurückgleiten.

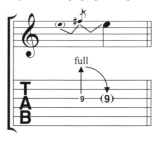

GLISSANDOTECHNIK MIT NACHFOLGENDEM ANSCHLAG: Gleiche Technik wie das gebundene Glissando, jedoch wird die zweite Note angeschlagen.

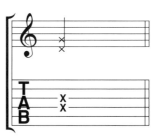

DÄMPFEN MIT DER GRIFFHAND: Du erreichst einen percussiven Sound, indem du die Griffhand leicht über die Saiten legst (ohne diese herunter-zudrücken) und dann mit der Schlaghand anschlägst.

AMMERKUNG: Das Tempo der Zieher und Glissandos ist abhängig von der rhythmischen Notation und dem Grundtempo.

1 2 3 4 5 6 7 8 9

CD Track Listing

Full instrumental performances (with guitar)...

1 Hold Me, Thrill Me, Kiss Me, Kill Me
2 Discothèque
3 Beautiful Day
4 Stuck In A Moment You Can't Get Out Of
5 Elevation (Tomb Raider Mix)
6 Last Night On Earth
7 Walk On

Backing tracks only (without guitar)...

8 Hold Me, Thrill Me, Kiss Me, Kill Me
9 Discothèque
10 Beautiful Day
11 Stuck In A Moment You Can't Get Out Of
12 Elevation (Tomb Raider Mix)
13 Last Night On Earth
14 Walk On

All tracks:
(U2) Blue Mountain Music Limited.

To remove your CD from the plastic sleeve, lift the small lip on the side to break the perforated strip. Replace the disc after use for convenient storage.